YOU CHOOSE
IF YOU LI

D0714664

PRISONER ESCAPE

SIMON CHAPMAN

First published in 2013
by Franklin Watts

Text © Simon Chapman 2013
Illustrations by David Cousens © Franklin Watts 2013

Franklin Watts
338 Euston Road
London NW1 3BH

Franklin Watts Australia
Level 17/207 Kent Street
Sydney, NSW 2000

A CIP catalogue record for this book
is available from the British Library.

(pb) ISBN: 978 1 4451 1361 6
(Library ebook) ISBN: 978 1 4451 2562 6
(ebook) ISBN: 978 1 4451 1365 4

1 3 5 7 9 10 8 6 4 2

Printed in Great Britain

Franklin Watts is a division of Hachette Children's Books,
an Hachette UK company.
www.hachette.co.uk

This book is not like others you may have read. YOU will decide if you live or die by making choices that affect how the adventure unfolds.

Each section of this book is numbered. At the end of most sections, you will have to make a choice. The choice you make will take you to a different section of the book.

Some of your choices will help you to survive the adventure. But choose carefully! The wrong decisions could cost you your life...

If you die, then go back to the chapter number you are given and learn from your mistake.

If you choose correctly, you will survive.

CHAPTER ONE

It's clear you only have one option now, you have to escape. No one believes you. Not the police, not the jury. Even Mr Whiteman, the well-meaning solicitor appointed to defend you, is struggling. You've been waiting in the cells of the courthouse for the last twenty minutes while the jury considers its verdict. It's time to make your move. You stuff your socks down the toilet in your cell and block it up. A quick flush, and there's water everywhere!

"Guard! Guard!" you call out.

The chunky guard curses and swears as he comes in and finds the floor flooded. He calls someone on his radio.

"You stay sitting there. I don't suppose you know what happened?" He glares at you.

"Hey, it just started bubbling up — but I do need the toilet," you say.

"Yeah, sure you do." He backs off to avoid getting his shiny shoes wet.

"I need to go, come on."

Finally, he handcuffs you to his wrist for the short walk to the toilets across the hallway. You've already worked out that you're on the first floor. Now to get the cuffs off.

"I'll stay with you," he says as you enter the bathroom.

"I need a number two," you answer.

"Jeez. All right. But don't try anything," the guard warns as he unlocks the cuffs and pushes you into the cubicle.

You drop your trousers and consider your situation. You really do need to pee.

Mr Whiteman told you to tell the truth, but what good has that done you? He knows you haven't got a hope. You think back, and remember the prosecution lawyer's face. Her words roll out like the script in a movie.

"So, let's go over this again," she says.

"A man, who you claim you don't know, puts a package with a gun into your bag. You later fire the gun and almost kill a government minister. And you say it was an accident," she says.

"Yes, it was an accident. I'd never seen the man before. As he walked past he must have slipped me the package. When I grabbed it to look inside, the gun went off. I didn't mean to pull the trigger."

"But you fired right at the minister. You were trying to kill him."

"No!" You grimace as you recall this bit. You shouldn't have lost your temper. "The man in the suit, it was his gun! Check the CCTV if you don't believe me!"

"But we've already seen the clip from the security tape at the station, and it shows lots of men in suits — but what it doesn't show is anyone 'slipping' you a gun." You remember how she deliberately

folded her arms at this point.

"What about the thing that fell out of the package when the police tackled me?" you snap back. "It was small and black, like an MP3 player."

"We have been over that too," said the laywer, pretending to be bored. "The police looked. They found nothing. What we have are the facts. At 5.19 p.m. at Central Station, a youth matching your description pulls a semi-automatic pistol out of a large padded envelope and fires the gun. The bullet — by some fluke — embeds itself in the bodywork of a train carriage, instead of killing the government minister. Moments later, two anti-terrorist officers arrest the youth — you — after what their statements say is a failed assassination attempt."

Whatever you said after that, it made no difference. That's why you're here. In the toilet. It's time to escape.

Survival Challenge: Escape from the courthouse

You pull up your trousers. There's a small window above the toilet. It will be tight, but you'll be able to squeeze through it if you can force it open.

The decisions you make now will decide whether you live or die.

You step up onto the toilet rim. You can't quite reach the window from here, so you'll have to stand on either side of the cubicle partition.

➜   If you want to flush the toilet before you climb up, go to 11.

➜   If you'd rather just climb up, go to 69.

1.
You sprint, dodging between the people in the station as a departing train is announced over the speakers, and everyone

surges forward. The two men are slow to react. You jump the barriers and reach the entrance, where there is a homeless man with a dog. You also spot a sign for the toilets.

➜ If you want to keep running out of the station, go to 75.

➜ If you want to sit down next to the musician and disguise yourself, go to 60.

➜ If you want to hide in the toilets, go to 83.

2.

You grab hold of the window ledge and slide your legs in through the window. The man sitting on the toilet below you gets the shock of his life! He has no time to react as you land on the floor in front of him, open the door and push through into a busy corridor with offices either side. Your heart is pounding as you look for possible escape routes. Near the lift there is a door labelled "Fire Exit".

➜ If you want to head through the fire exit and down the stairs, go to 76.

➜ If you decide to head through the fire exit and up the stairs, go to 52.

3.

You land with a thud on the roof of a green car and slide down the windscreen onto the ground. A police officer armed with a taser is clambering across the railing into the traffic.

➜ To run away from the police officer, out into the faster traffic, go to 28.

➜ To run along the line of stationary cars, away from the roadblock, go to 48.

4.

As you approach the electric car, one of the suits moves round to fire on you. Is there an angel on your shoulder? Find out by choosing either 25 or 42.

5.

You slop through the water, the helicopter still shining its powerful light down on you. The light is actually quite useful, helping you to avoid debris in the water, but you can hear that police dog barking, and it

3

4

5

seems very close now.

➜   To duck under the water, go to 71.

➜   To climb out of the ditch on the other side and run towards the overpass, go to 43.

6.

You push through the door and into the car park. It runs like a gigantic spiral on one side of the shopping mall. Rows of cars line the sides, with a corkscrew-style ramp allowing cars to drive up and down the levels. You hop onto the skateboard, and push off down the ramp. There's a scream from behind you and the sound of a gunshot, but you don't turn to see what's happening. You pick up speed down the ramp. Suddenly you're aware of the roar of a car engine behind you — and it's getting closer!

➜   If you want to swerve to one side, go to 39.

➜   If you want to turn to look behind you, go to 16.

7.

You scoot back into the darkness of the garage and cover yourself with old boxes. The thwack-thwack noise of the helicopter seems very loud now, and you hardly hear the police at the entrance until a dog starts barking. They have a sniffer dog with them!

"Show yourself, or we'll send in the dog!" There's no escape for you. The police take you back into custody.

➜ The next day the jury find you guilty, and you are remanded in custody to await sentencing. Go back to Chapter 3.

8.

Luckily the woman driving the car spots you, and you manage to whizz past her car as she brakes. You've nearly reached the bottom of the twisting ramp, but the suit's car is still slightly behind you on the other side. Ahead you can see the entrance barrier is down and the exit barrier is up.

➜ If you wish to crouch down under the

barrier, go to 77.

➜ If you'd rather go through the open exit barrier, go to 90.

9.

You start walking towards the police officers as a woman — about your mum's age — overtakes you. She's obviously in a hurry.

➜ To carry on walking alone, go to 54.

➜ To follow on closely behind the woman, as though she is your mum, go to 78.

10.

You look around and see the pager just as it is kicked away from you across the concourse. If you stay out in the open much longer you risk being shot by the suits or the police, but you have to get the pager back! You can only see one of the suits. He's hiding in the gift shop.

➜ To get to cover behind a row of trolleys behind you, go to 68.

➜   To run across the empty concourse to get the pager, go to 32.

11.
Flushing the toilet makes just enough noise to mask the scrabbling of your trainers as you clamber up the side of the cubicle. Go to 26.

12.
The dog bites your arm as you attempt to shield your face from its teeth. The weight of the animal drags you down, and before you know it, a policeman has hold of you.
➜   You've been caught! The next day the jury find you guilty, and you are remanded in custody to await sentencing. Go back to Chapter 3.

13.
You send the message, and in an instant the whole station shudders. There is a violent explosion and a giant ball of flame gushes

along the train track. The fireball swirls out
across the concourse engulfing everything
in its path. The blast shatters the glass-
panelled roof, and the last thing you see is
glittering shards as they rain down through
the smoke and fire.

➜   You've come to the end of your
challenge. Get back to Chapter 6 to finish
the job properly.

14.

You turn, push through the skateboarders, and step onto the "down" escalator. But it's taking you down right past the suit coming up — and now he's spotted you! You turn around. The skateboarders have just got on, making it impossible to run back up the "down" escalator, leaving you only two escape routes.

➡   To jump over to the "up" escalator, where the two pass in the middle, go to 74.

➡   To run to the bottom of the "down" escalator you are on, go to 46.

15.

You dash over and use the side wall of the garages to boost yourself up onto the fence. From here you clamber onto the roof of the garages as the police helicopter searchlight picks you out in the dark. You lower yourself down on the other side of the fence and start to sprint across the rough ground littered with rubbish and stunted bushes. In front of you there is an embankment with a train line running out of the city. Over to the right, the railway sidings run under the overpass of a major road.

➜ If you want to run towards the embankment and the train line, go to 24.

➜ If you want to run under the overpass, go to 79.

16.

You turn to see a car behind you, driven by the suit from the station. He has an evil look on his face, and before you can do anything else, he knocks you down.

➜ You don't survive your injuries. Get back to Chapter 5 — don't hang around!

17.

You run to the edge of the building and then leap over the gap. You crash down onto the flat roof and skid across the surface. Quickly, you jump to your feet and look for a route off the roof.

There's a roof access door further along behind a ventilation duct. Just before you go through it, you glance over your shoulder. On the courthouse roof you can see several policemen talking into their communications radios.

CHAPTER TWO

You've escaped, but now you're on the run. The wail of police sirens is closing in from all directions. Once on the ground you throw off your suit jacket, duck into a side street and quickly head away from the courthouse. You know the police are after you. They'll lay down a cordon several streets around the court building and try to trap you. You have to get out of the area. You have to find the man who gave you the gun! You stop dead in your tracks.

At the end of the street you can see a strip of police tape, and there's a police van. You move back onto a busier road, blending in with the crowds, but up ahead you can see more police officers, and some of them have dogs.

You look around for an exit. You can't head back towards the courthouse, but perhaps you could head up again — above ground level. You walk on, before turning into an alleyway. You stand on a bin to reach the ladder of a fire escape, and pull yourself up. You're quickly on the roof, and travelling past the police checkpoint. You hardly have to jump between buildings here — everything has been so closely built together in the city. Below you can hear more sirens, and you can't help but take a peek.

Look at them all! They've no idea where you are! You jump down onto a roof terrace garden and then leap across onto the roof of a row of apartments. All too soon you're out of luck; you reach the end of the roof.

You look around, and then spot some scaffolding. You jog over to it. It leads down to the street where a wide intersection is filled with vehicles. The two outbound lanes closest to you are moving slowly as they pass through a police roadblock. The other four lanes into the

city centre are moving more quickly. All of
your options are on the other side of the
road. There's a housing estate, with lots of
places where you could tuck yourself away
while the police run round in circles.

Survival Challenge: Slipping through the net

Below you there are several metal gantries
spanning the six lanes. These are frames
supporting the direction signs that tell
drivers which lane to be in. If you get
across to the gantry from the scaffolding,
you might be in with a chance of getting
across the road without being seen. You
begin the climb down the scaffolding.

As you get closer to the ground a
workman spots you on the scaffolding.

"Oi, you! You can't be climbing about up
here!" His voice gets the attention of the
police officers below. You've been spotted!

The decisions you make now will decide whether you live or die.

You quickly span the gap between the scaffolding and the gantry by lying a ladder down across it. You balance across carefully, as police officers on the ground rush towards you. You know you'll have to move fast before the officers can block you off on the other side. You'll have to push caution aside.

➡ If you wish to clamber across the gantry quickly, go to 72.

➡ If you'd prefer to swing down onto one of the stationary cars below, go to 3.

18.

As you pass the gap, you can see several police officers are crossing through stationary traffic below. You're over the third lane when you hear a voice over a loudhailer.

"Stop! You cannot escape. We have you surrounded — don't do anything that will make this worse for you." You have to keep moving! Go to 82.

19.

You grab hold of the car door and duck down. The driver can't see you here! But, he doesn't need to, he just simply moves over to the left and crushes you up against the car park ramp wall.

➜   You don't survive your injuries. Get back to Chapter 5 — and don't mess up!

20.

The kiosk owner is suspicious of you — you can't stay here long. You look back along the platform and spot a sign for the toilets.

➜   If you decide to try walking past the police officers, go to 9.
➜   If you want to hide in the toilets, go to 83.

21.

You push down on the bar of the fire escape and burst out onto the roof. You can hear more shouts behind you as the police officers chase after you. At the far end of the roof you can see that the next building along also has a flat roof, and is at a slightly lower level. You'd have to jump a gap of about three metres or so.

➜ If you want to run and attempt to jump the gap to the next building, go to 17.

➜ If you want to look for another way off the roof, go to 36.

22.

You decide to take a chance that the man hasn't spotted you. You carry on walking — and he goes straight past! But almost as soon as you think you've escaped, a rough hand presses over your mouth and wrenches your arm backwards. The suit recognised you from the station! He drags you over to the car and bundles you into the boot. He slams the lid, and you are never seen again.

➜ You won't go to prison, but you also failed to survive! Get back to Chapter 5.

23.

"Please, help me," you ask the woman. She scowls at you.

"Keep away from me, freak!" the woman says loudly. The police officers look over and head straight towards you. Go to 75.

24.

You run towards the embankment, but the light of the helicopter picks out a fence at the bottom. You can't get up the embankment without climbing over it.

➜ To climb up the fence, go to 31.

➜ If you would prefer to jump down into the ditch, go to 89.

25.

The suit now has a clear line of sight, and there's nothing you can do as he opens fire on your unprotected body.

➜ You've come to the end of your challenge. Get back to Chapter 6 to finish the job properly.

26.

You force open the window and, pulling yourself up, you begin to squeeze through. There's no sign that the guard has heard you do this. You twist round and grip the window ledge above to help pull your legs through. You're now outside, hanging onto the ledge. About six metres below is the car park where prisoners are brought into the courthouse. To your right there is a strong-looking drainpipe.

➜   If you want to swing over and slide down the drainpipe into the car park, go to 88.

➜   If you want to swing over and climb up the drainpipe, go to 40.

27.

Panic grips you now. All you can think to do is shout for help. The two officers with the photo come rushing over.

"Help me, please," you say.

"Oh, we'll help you all right. This is the one we're looking for! You're coming with us." Your hands are cuffed, and you're led out of the station.

➜   The next day the jury find you guilty, and you are remanded in custody to await sentencing. Go back to Chapter 4.

28.

You run into one of the lanes where cars are travelling faster. A horn blares and your arm is clipped by a wing mirror. You dodge a couple of cars that slow down, but then there is a screech of brakes as you step in front of a van. The driver swears at you out of his window. You check over your shoulder. The police officer is waving at cars to stop them. You still have two lanes to cross before you get to the other side.

➜ If you want to step out around the van, go to 87.

➜ If you want to run down the line of queuing traffic, go to 48.

29.

A bullet catches you in the shoulder, sending you spinning to the ground.

➜ You won't go to prison, but you also failed to survive! Get back to Chapter 5.

30.

You push through a hole in the fence to the housing estate, and race for the cover of a nearby building. The police are nowhere to be seen. You keep running until you are exhausted. You have to rest.

CHAPTER THREE

It's late. You've found a place to hide in a lock-up garage — part of a row of them backing onto some railway sidings. There doesn't seem to be anyone else around, and everything is quiet apart from the occasional train rumbling past and the distant wail of a siren. You know you need to find the mystery man who slipped the gun into your bag, but you can't work out how. The problem ticks over in your mind until you can't stay awake any longer. You close your eyes and drift off to sleep.

Survival Challenge: On the run

Perhaps it is a change in the background noise that wakes you. There is a dog barking, and you can also hear a helicopter hovering overhead. There are voices too, instructions being given out. There's no doubt, the police are searching the area for you!

The decisions you make now will decide whether you live or die.

Your body feels stiff and cold, but the fear in your stomach gets you up quickly. You peer round the corner of the garage.

It's dark except for the light of some streetlamps. There are at least six police officers with torches heading in your direction. Suddenly, the beam of the helicopter searchlight floods the building directly opposite.

➜ If you decide to go back into the garage and hide under some cardboard boxes, go to 7.

➜ If you want to sneak across the road behind one of the parked cars, go to 50.

➜ If you want to leave the garage and get to the fence at the back leading to the railway, go to 15.

31.

You start to scale the fence, but the rusted wire cuts into your hands. Even when you get to the top, your shirt gets snagged on some barbed wire, and you struggle to free your arm. Without warning, you are dragged backwards and flung to the ground.

"It's the end of the line for you," the

police officer says, a big grin sweeping across his face.

➜ The next day the jury find you guilty, and you are remanded in custody to await sentencing. Go back to Chapter 3.

32.
You don't move fast enough. A bullet catches you in the chest and your lifeless body falls to the floor.

➜ You've been shot! Get back to Chapter 6 and don't make the same mistake next time!

33.
You swivel round on top of the cubicle wall and lash out with your foot. You catch the guard in the chest and he stumbles backwards before falling to the floor. You need to get out of here, fast! You quickly change your plan, jumping down from the wall and heading for the toilet door. Outside the busy corridor is full of court

officials carrying papers. You can see a door next to the lift labelled "Fire Exit".

→ If you want to head through the fire exit and down the stairs, go to 76.

→ If you want to head through the fire exit and up the stairs, go to 52.

34.

You head straight towards the men, clenching your fists as you ready yourself. You wait until the last possible moment before swinging a punch. It catches the man you recognise right on the chin. He staggers back and then simply grins. The other man steps forward and quickly puts his arm over your shoulder, pulling you against him tightly. You can hardly breathe!

"You have a very strong fist. But now I think you are coming with us." They've been watching you, and now they want the pager!

→ If you decide to shout, "Police, help!", go to 27.

➜   If you want to try something else, go
to 64.

35.
You jump onto the driver's cab, but the
roof is metal and you land with a thud.
The driver slams on the brakes in surprise,
and you are sent tumbling off the roof. You
smash into the back of a car travelling in
front, and despite the best efforts of the
paramedic crew that arrives shortly after,
you don't make it to your trial.
➜   You have died. Get back to Chapter 2.

36.
You run around the edge of the building,
but you've missed your chance to escape!
The officers soon catch up with you, and
pin you down as they fasten handcuffs
around your wrists.
➜   You've failed to escape, and are taken
back to your holding cell. The jury find you
guilty, and you are remanded in custody to
await sentencing. Go back to Chapter 1.

37.

A woman crashes into a display stand at the skate shop. As you bend down to grab a new skateboard, another bullet zips overhead. Luck was on your side! You race towards the exit to the Level 3 car park with the board tucked under your arm. Go to 6.

38.

You duck down and crouch in the drain outlet — there is a wire mesh screen stopping you from going too far down. You huddle in the darkness, wet and cold. After a while, you hear voices over the thudding noise of the helicopter above.

"We know you're in there. I really don't want to get my feet wet, so if you come out now I'll keep the dog on the leash."

➜ You've run out of options. You've failed to find the mystery man, and are taken back into custody. At your trial the jury find you guilty. Go back to Chapter 3.

39.

You swerve just in time! A car accelerates up behind you and attempts to knock you down. You quickly perform an ollie up onto the narrow kerb, dragging your arm against the concrete wall. You know you won't be able to outrun the car, but maybe you can outthink the man driving it.

➜   If you want to stop suddenly, go to 53.

➜   If you want to jump over onto the "up" lane of the ramp, go to 65.

➜   If you want to grab the car door handle, go to 19.

40.

You swing over and then start the careful climb up the drainpipe. It's slippery, but you manage to hold on. There is an open toilet window on the next floor up.

➜   If you want to climb in through the window, go to 2.

➜   If you want to continue up to the roof of the building, go to 62.

39

40

41.

You duck and the dog crashes into the access ladder, knocking itself out. Go to 30.

42.

You duck down and drag the trolleys past the electric car. You can now see the two suits crouching down behind it, with the trolleys shielding you from both them and the police. You force the trolleys on until you can reach out and grab the pager.

➜ If you want to use it to threaten the two armed men, go to 80.

➜ If you want to use the pager to send the message "execute", go to 13.

43.

You pull yourself out of the filthy water and run as fast as you can towards the overpass. Your trousers stick to your legs, and the blisters on your feet rub against your shoes. You wish you had your socks back! Somewhere behind you the police dog is barking, but you can't tell how close it is. Up ahead, under the overpass, you can see a large group of people and hear music playing. You run over towards them. Go to 59.

44.

"Look, there's Gran." You point at some random old woman on the other side of the concourse. "Gran!" you shout loudly, waving your arm. Almost every old lady turns to look at you, including the woman you pointed towards. "Mum, can I go over to her?" you ask. The woman looks back at you as if you're mad, but keeps walking. "Thanks, Mum." You smile back. By then you've passed the police officers! Go to 67.

45.

You run across to the accessway, into the darkness beyond. You hear the door squeal closed behind you, and then a bolt sliding across, locking you in.

CHAPTER FOUR

"Shhh!" the man's voice says. But you're out of breath, and it's hard to breathe quietly. It's completely dark inside and you quickly notice a strong, stale smell. The music outside suddenly stops and you can hear the thump of the helicopter again. You jump when someone bangs on the door, but the bolt holds firm.

You wait for what seems like ages before the man speaks again.

"I was watchin' you. You gave them police a good runnin'." He strikes a match, casting enough light for you to see your surroundings.

You size up your rescuer. He has a weathered face and is wearing a long coat and a tatty beany. The stale smell is coming from him. There's a pile of flattened cardboard boxes on the floor

close to his feet, a sleeping bag and some plastic bags containing what you guess are his belongings. The small room isn't much bigger than a toilet cubicle and has a ladder mounted on one wall leading upwards.

"Er ... thanks," you mumble. "But I have to go."

The man's hand grips your shoulder. "Hey, not so fast. The police might still be out there." He lights a candle with the match and sits down. "Rest up a bit."

You are unsure whether you should run for it right now, but he does have a point. The police will probably still be in the area. "The name's Duggie," the man says. "You hungry?"

You realise you haven't eaten for hours, so you sit down. He passes you an out-of-date pot of supermarket pasta and a plastic fork. "Luxury, this is. You wouldn't believe the food people chuck out." He tucks into his own pot.

"Why did you help me?" you ask after you've told Duggie your name.

"I've no love for the police," the man answers. "Nor would I have helped you if I had thought I was going to get caught. What did you do?"

You tell him your story, how a well-dressed man slipped a package into your bag, how you nearly shot a government minister by accident, and the MP3 player.

"So, what are you going to do?"

"Try to find the man, but I don't know where to start."

"What about the thingy-bob that you say fell out of your bag when you were arrested? If you find that, maybe it will lead you to the man."

You can't believe you hadn't thought of

this yourself. The MP3 player! If the police didn't find it, maybe the man didn't either. It could still be at the station! This thought fills you with renewed hope.

"But if you ask me," Duggie says, "I think it's only a matter of time before you get caught. You gotta think smart like me."

You've decided. "I'm going back to Central Station. But there's something I need you to do for me, Duggie. I can't contact my mum, but you can." You ask Duggie to take a message to your mum, and he agrees. "Now that's smart thinking," he says.

The police are long gone by the time you begin to walk back into the city in the early hours. Duggie lent you his beany and an old rain mac. Now you look like any other very scruffy kid — even if you do smell a bit. You keep off the main streets and keep moving, stopping only to swipe a pair of socks from the balcony washing line of a ground-floor apartment.

You arrive outside Central Station, and from across the street you wait to see if there are any police on patrol. If the police are here, you can't see them. While you were walking you hatched a plan. You know there will be CCTV cameras, so you'll have to work fast. But posing as a homeless person will give you a little more time. You have to find the MP3 player! You tie your hoodie around your waist, but keep your mac on, and wait for the opportunity to get through the station ticket barriers.

Survival Challenge: Central Station

You don't have to wait long. A woman with her four children are more than enough to distract the ticket inspector as he opens the barrier for her buggy. Once inside the station, you head casually to the platform where you were arrested.

You loiter in a camera blind spot, looking at the platform and trying to think back. When the MP3 player tumbled out you remember seeing it, and then it had simply vanished. But no one was nearby to snatch it, so...

Then you see something. A metal grille set into the platform. Could the MP3 player have slipped down there? You scuff your feet as you move over, then bend down next to the grille as you pretend to tie your shoelace.

The gaps in the metal look big enough for something to fall through, in fact you can see a mound of litter at the bottom of the duct. Using your mac as cover, you lift up the grille and reach down, sifting through the rubbish with your hand. You touch something hard and plastic, grab it, and pull it out. It's the object you remember from your bag, but it's not an MP3 player. You replace the grille, and look at the plastic rectangle as you stand up. It's an old-fashioned beeper — a pager like the ones used by doctors, with an LCD screen that displays scrolling messages.

But you don't have time to investigate it further. Two armed police officers are patrolling the main concourse, and they are headed straight towards you.

The decisions you make now will decide whether you live or die.

The two officers are walking slowly through the station occasionally stopping passers-by and showing them a photo of something. They stop one man, who looks at the photo, then shakes his head and walks off.

➔ If you want to act casually, and try to walk past them, go to 9.

➔ If you want to walk over to a newspaper kiosk, and try to look inconspicuous, go to 20.

46.

You speed down the steps, but just as you reach the bottom, the man who slipped you the gun steps across your path. "There is no escape for you this time," he says.

➜ You won't go to prison, but you also failed to survive! Get back to Chapter 5.

47.

You jump up and start to pull yourself through the small window. But it's a tight squeeze, and before you can get even halfway you feel the guard grab your legs from the other side. He's a big man with a tight grip, and he pulls you back through easily. He drops you to the floor in a heap, then quickly slaps the handcuffs back on your wrists.

➜ Your escape is over before it started! You're taken back to your holding cell. The jury find you guilty, and you are remanded in custody to await sentencing. Go back to Chapter 1.

48.

You head down the line of cars, but as you approach one car, the driver swings the door open. You crash into it and fall backwards. A policeman steps out of his unmarked police car as the officer behind you shouts, "Taser, taser, taser!" The next thing you know, 1,200 volts pass through your body, causing you to completely collapse.

➜ You failed to escape. The jury later find you guilty, and you are remanded in custody to await sentencing. Go back to Chapter 2.

49.

You dash out from behind the luggage trolleys, but you don't make it to the electric car. A police marksman targets you and your whole world suddenly turns black and still.

➜ You've been killed by the police in the confusion. Get back to Chapter 6.

50.

You dart across the road and take cover behind a car. You can now see the police officers are sweeping the torch beams onto the garage doors and the buildings across the way. One officer is gripping the leash of a police sniffer dog.

➜ To hide where you are, go to 66.

➜ To hide back in the garage, go to 7.

➜ To sneak back across the road to the fence and the railway sidings, go to 15.

51.

You walk over to the chair and casually pick up the board, without the skaters spotting you. The suit is near to the top of the "up" escalator, so you quickly head for the exit to the level 3 car park. Just as you turn, another suit appears from the exit door — he's one you saw at Central Station — but he's headed around the other side of the level. You make a move for the glass door while you can. Go to 6.

52.

You push through the fire exit and begin the climb up the stairs. Further down the stairwell you can hear police radios crackling and people barking orders. They must have realised you've escaped! You're almost at the top of the stairs, when the fire exit door next to you opens and a policeman appears. You quickly shove him

in the chest, then rush up the last few stairs, which lead to the roof. Go to 21.

53.
You grind your shoe against the concrete floor and the car shoots past. The driver slams on the brakes and flings open his door. He pulls a gun from his shoulder holster. Whether you can get away before he shoots you will be something only fate can decide. Choose either 29 or 65.

54.
As you approach the officers, one holds out a photo towards you.

"Can you help us? We're looking for someone about your age. Have you..." the policewoman starts.

➜   To run past them, towards the station exit, go to 75.

➜   To act naturally and look at the photo, go to 86.

55.

You dive across into a shop, only to find that one of the suits has taken up a firing position inside. The instant he sees you he shifts his position.

➜ If you want to hide further inside the shop, go to 32.

➜ To leave the shop and crouch down behind a row of luggage trolleys outside, go to 68.

56.

You drop through the gap onto the top of the trailer. You immediately lie flat as the lorry begins to edge forwards. The police officers rush past — they can't see you from down on the ground. You soon realise though that if you stay up here the lorry will drive back towards the courthouse. You have to make a move. You could jump down onto the driver's cab and then get down, or you could swing out over the side and lower yourself down using one of the straps on the trailer.

→   To jump onto the driver's cab, go to 35.

→   To climb down using a strap, go to 63.

57.

Suddenly the cubicle door crashes open behind you and the guard charges in.

"Where do you think you're going?"

→   If you want to kick the guard to slow him down, go to 33.

→   If you want to push open the window and climb through, go to 47.

58.

You jog over to the car park exit, but on the other side of the glass door you can see one of the suits from Central Station. He's just parked a car and is walking over towards you!

→   If you want to push through the door, go to 22.

→   If you want to go back and take the escalator down to Level 2, go to 14.

59.

Your legs are heavy and your lungs are aching as you reach the group of people. You know you haven't got the energy to run much further. Up ahead teenagers are skateboarding on the concrete ramps

underneath the overpass. Music is blasting out of a nearby car. You run between the headlights — the skateboarders don't pay you any attention. You manage to swipe a dark-coloured hoodie as you pass. You pull it on over your shirt as a voice says, "Quick! Get in here."

You can see an access door is open, and a hand waving you inside.

➜   To enter the access door, go to 45.

➜   To hide behind the car, go to 66.

60.

You quickly take off the mac, sit on it and bring your hood down low over your eyes. The man with the dog simply looks at you and smiles. Moments later, the two men run past without even noticing you. You wait and thank the man. "No problem. Any friend of Duggie's is a friend of mine." You don't stop to wonder how he knows about Duggie. You check the exit again and slip out as a crowd of tourists leave.

CHAPTER FIVE

Your experience at Central Station has taught you that it is easy to get lost in a crowd, so you head to King Street Mall. You check to make sure you're not being followed. The two suits are nowhere to be seen.

Some skateboarders are trying out moves outside the mall, so with your hood up you sit down to watch. You take the chance to look at the pager in more detail. Why do those men want it so much?

You press a button and it comes out of sleep mode. You press an arrow key to scroll through the inbox messages, but there aren't any. In fact, the only thing on the beeper is a saved message which has not been sent. It simply reads "execute". Does sending the message do something? You decide to send a message of your own

to Mr Whiteman, your lawyer. You have the evidence you need to at least put a stop to your trial. You just need to get it into the right hands. You pull out Mr Whiteman's business card from your pocket and message his mobile phone: *I am innocent. The man who gave me the gun was in Central Station today. Come and pick me up from King St Mall now.*

After a while the skateboard crew move off into the shopping mall and you tag along. There's a skate gear shop on the top level — Level 3. You decide that as there are a couple of cafés where you could swipe some leftover food, this is a good place to go until Mr Whiteman arrives.

It's when you're on the way up the escalator to Level 3 that you spot trouble. The man who gave you the gun is on the level below, handing some cash to Duggie! That two-faced dropout! He must have told the suits where to find you — he set you up! That's why the suits were waiting at Central Station! You reach the top level, grab a half-eaten croissant from a plate, and look around for an escape route. That's when you spot one of the suits coming up the escalator to Level 3. You're sure he hasn't spotted you yet.

Survival Challenge: King Street Mall

There's a door marked "Exit — Car Park Level 3" just beyond the skater boys, who are milling around at the top of a "down" escalator. One of them has left his skateboard propped up against a café chair.

The decisions you make now will decide whether you live or die.

➜ If you want to head to the car park exit door, go to 58.

➜ If you want to take the escalator down to Level 2, go to 14.

➜   If you want to grab the skater's board by the chair, go to 51.

61.
You grab a group of trolleys, and with a shove you get them rolling. Keeping your back to the gift shop you steer them towards the electric car. From here you can now see the pager!
➜   To keep rolling towards the electric car, go to 4.
➜   To push the trolleys past the electric car, towards the pager, go to 42.

62.
You are on a flat roof. The court building makes up four sides of a large square, with a courtyard on one side and the car park on the other, four floors below. The only other ways down are through a door behind you, marked "Stairs", or a jump to another flat roof on the next building. You guess it's about three metres away.

61

62

➡ To head over to the door, go to 73.
➡ To run and attempt to jump the gap to the next building, go to 17.

63.

Cautiously, you lower yourself down to the road, watching all the time for police. You can hear a dog barking somewhere nearby. It looks as though all the traffic has now been stopped in an attempt to find you. You crouch down low, and weave between the cars, heading at a diagonal across the road. There's just not enough police officers on the ground to cover the whole intersection, and you make it to the other side unseen. Go to 30.

64.

These men seem to think you've given up! You slam your fist back and up into the man's groin and he grunts loudly, releasing his grip a fraction. It's all you need. Before the other man can react, you bolt away. Go to 1.

65.

You push off hard and speed forward on the skateboard. You jump over the barrier as the skateboard runs underneath and amazingly land back on the board! But you don't have time to congratulate yourself — there's a car speeding up the ramp towards you! Go to 8.

66.

You tuck yourself in against the car. A torch beam casts a shadow of the car on the wall next to you. The police officers walk past, and you think you've managed to trick them, but then the dog starts to bark. You sink down, wishing you could turn invisible, when a large policeman stands over you.

"Not feeling so clever now, are we?" he says smugly.

➜ The next day the jury find you guilty, and you are remanded in custody to await sentencing. Go back to Chapter 3.

67.

You head towards the smiling old lady, away from the police officers. It's then you notice two well-dressed men. They start to walk straight towards you, over from where they were standing watching you. You almost come to a stop as panic sweeps through you. One of the men — he's the man who slipped you the gun!

→ If you decide to run, go to 1.

→ If you decide to fight them, go to 34.

→ If you decide to shout, "Police, help!", go to 27.

68.

As you move, the air where you were just standing fills with bullets. The man in the shop is shooting right at you! Now police firearms officers have begun to target the three armed men. You get down behind the trolleys and have time to assess the situation. Go to 84.

69.

Your shoes scuff the sides of the cubicle as you clamber up, and the partition squeaks loudly.

"Come on, hurry it up! What's going on in there?" the guard outside asks. You begin to force the window.

→ To answer the guard, go to 81.

→ To simply ignore him, go to 57.

68

69

70.

The two armed men argue with each other, before they throw down their guns and put their hands in the air. You are about to step out from behind the trolleys, when someone barks at you from over your shoulder. "Drop your weapon and get

down on the floor!" A police officer has
a gun pointing right at you. You do as he
says, lying flat on the cold concourse floor.
Another officer cuffs your hands behind
your back.

"You're under arrest," he says.

"Not for long. I'm innocent," you reply.
"And now I can prove it." Go to 91.

71.

You duck under the water in the hope that
the dog will just run past. But the muck
stings your eyes and you can only hold your
breath for a short while. You rise up again
slowly. The helicopter is hovering right
above you, and two policemen are standing
at the top of the ditch. One shines a torch
in your face.

"You having a nice swim?" he says,
before they drag you out of the filthy water.

➜   You've failed to find the mystery man,
and are taken back into custody. At your
trial the jury find you guilty. Go back to
Chapter 3.

72.

You stay on the gantry and move across it as quickly as you can. You duck under crossbeams and vault over lower supporting struts. Below, you can hear car tyres squealing and voices shouting. The police are coming after you by crossing the road! You come to a gap in the gantry-mounted lane signs where you could drop down onto the covered trailer of a lorry, which has stopped below.

➔   If you want to drop down onto the lorry trailer, go to 56.

➔   If you want to carry on across the lanes, towards the other side of the road, go to 18.

73.

You turn to head over to the door just as two policemen open it. "Oi! You! Stop right there!"

You decide not to do as they ask!

➔   To run and attempt to jump the gap

to the next building, go to 17.

➜ To look for another way off the roof, go to 36.

74.
You grab the handrail and leap across the gap to the "up" escalator, taking the suit completely by surprise. He reaches for something tucked inside his jacket, but before he can pull it out you shove him backwards. He tumbles down the steps of the escalator. You bound back up to level 3 as a gunshot rings out behind you. They're shooting at you! People in the mall scream and run for cover, blocking your path. Only luck will decide if you make it now. Choose either 29 or 37.

75.
All you can think to do is run. You make a break for the station exit.

"Hey, you! Hold it right there!" someone shouts from behind you. You barge through a crowd of tourists and straight out of the station. But before you can blink, a huge hand grabs you by the scruff of the neck and hoists you into the back of a waiting van.

➜ You've failed to survive! Get back to Chapter 4 — and try to avoid getting caught next time!

76.

You push the door open and bound down the stairs. You can almost taste freedom! But you come to a sudden halt — there is a policeman guarding the stairs and he has spotted you!

"Hey, you!" he shouts. You try to run back up the stairs, but he's too quick. He grabs your foot and drags you down the steps. "Let's get you back where you belong."

➜ You've failed to escape, and are taken back to your holding cell. The jury find you guilty, and you are remanded in custody to await sentencing. Go back to Chapter 1.

77.

You feel your hair brush against the barrier as you roll underneath it. Moments later, there is an echoing crash behind you. As the driver passed through the open barrier, it came down and smashed the car windscreen! You cruise out into the street, hoping that Mr Whiteman and the police are nearby. You head for the most public place you know — Central Station.

CHAPTER SIX

There are still at least two suits after you, but running on foot they are a lot slower than you. By the time you get to Central Station you're well ahead of them, but feeling pretty exhausted. You summon the last of your strength as you push behind a geeky-looking man and through the ticket barriers. You are going to prove your innocence today. Or you are going to die in the attempt.

You walk onto the concourse, in full view of the CCTV cameras. This time you want them to see you. You can't see any police officers patrolling — which you think is odd — as you reach into your pocket and pull out the pager. Standing out in the open, it doesn't take long for you to be spotted. Three men, one of them the gangster who slipped you the gun package, are walking towards you. You know they are armed, but right now any weapons they are carrying are hidden. All three men look uncomfortable.

"Give it to me now," the man says. "No more games."

"You could shoot me."

"Here? I don't think so. Just hand it over."

The men seem very tense.

You hold out the pager, as though you intend to hand it over, then snatch it back at the last second.

"What if I send the message 'execute'?" you ask.

The man looks scared now. "That would be very foolish," he replies.

For an instant there is stillness, like a pause in time. This is the bit where the police are meant to step in and save you, but perhaps Mr Whiteman never received your message, and hasn't followed you. There are still passengers on the concourse and the information panel is flicking up information on the next departure.

"Look. I am a fair man. Give me the device, we will walk away and we'll never meet again."

"I'll press send."

"Why would you do such a thing?"

His next action is unexpected, and far too quick for you. He lunges forward. At the same time, one of his henchmen moves in from the side. Caught by surprise, you spring backwards and the pager slips from your fingers. In slow motion, you see it tumbling through the air, the two henchmen diving for it. The pager bounces on the floor, skidding off into a mass of people. For an instant the pager is out of sight amongst their feet. At the same time an amplified voice blares out.

"This is the police!" All three men pull out their guns.

Survival Challenge: Into the fire

One henchman has an Uzi machine pistol. It buzzes as he fires on a squad of tactical police officers entering the station. People scream around you, and trip and stumble as

they flee. You duck down and see that you
could easily hide in a gift shop from here.

The decisions you make now will decide whether you live or die.

➜   If you want to follow some other
people into the gift shop, go to 55.
➜   If you think you should stay on the
concourse to find the pager, go to 10.

78.
The police are looking for a kid on their
own, so walking with the woman might
help you. You catch up with the woman and
walk alongside her.
➜   If you want to ask for the woman's
help, go to 23.
➜   If you want to pretend you know her,
go to 44.

79.
You decide that the overpass offers
the best chance of evading the police

helicopter, and you run towards it. The 'copter is hovering overhead. You've seen enough of those TV programmes to know that they are equipped with thermal imaging cameras. Even in the dark they'd be able to see you. Behind you there is the sound of a dog barking. The police must be sending the sniffer dog after you! As you get closer to the overpass you can see a ditch running parallel with the railway track.

➜   To keep running towards the overpass, go to 85.

➜   To head for the ditch, go to 89.

➜   To run towards the embankment and the train line after all, go to 24.

80.
You shout out as loud as you can, "Give yourselves up, or I'll send 'execute'." The two remaining suits look at each other.

"If you do you will send us all into the next life!" the leader shouts back.

"What have I got left to lose — you know they'll find me guilty. I'm not going to prison!" you yell.

"Put down your weapons!" a voice shouts over the loudhailer. "There is no escape, we have the entire station surrounded."
Go to 70.

81.
"Nothing," you answer. "Just a minute."
You reach up and start to force open the window, but you'll have to rely on luck to see if the guard believes you. Choose either 26 or 57.

82.
You reach the end of the gantry and begin to climb down the access ladder as quickly as possible. You know the traffic won't hold up the police for long. You jump down to the ground just as a snarling police dog lunges at you. You have to make a snap decision! Choose either 12 or 41.

83.

You head straight for the toilet sign and lock yourself in a cubicle. It feels like you're back in the courthouse again. You hear the main door open and hold your breath as someone comes in. The cubicle door crashes in and knocks you down. You look up and straight into the eyes of the man who slipped you the gun. "I want something you have," he says in a threatening voice. He catches you across the face with an open hand, but it's enough to crack your head against the wall and knock you out.

➜ You've failed to survive! Get back to Chapter 4 — and try to avoid getting caught next time!

84.

Sheltering behind the trolleys, you spot both the leader and his other henchman. They are firing from behind an electric car used to transport elderly passengers to the

trains. The police have taken up positions just inside the station entrance, but none of them can fire on you. The man in the gift shop suddenly cries out and stops shooting. The only thing you can't see from here is the pager, but you know it was somewhere behind the electric car.

➡ To run over and hide on the other side of the electric car, go to 49.

➡ To attempt to push the trolleys and move towards the electric car, go to 61.

85.

You run straight for the overpass, but even with your head start there's no way you can outrun a police dog. The Alsatian snarls at your heels, before grabbing your trousers. You crash down into the dirt and the dog locks onto your leg. You cry out in pain as the officers approach to take you back into custody.

➡ The next day the jury find you guilty, and you are remanded in custody to await sentencing. Go back to Chapter 3.

86.

"... seen this person?" she says. You look at the photo — it's a picture of you! "It looks a bit like me," you comment, "but it's not. Sorry, I have to go to meet ... my gran. Look, there she is." You point to some random old woman on the other side of the concourse, and start walking. Go to 67.

87.

You step out around the van just as a car speeds past. It strikes you, hurling you into the air and you land with a wet thud back down on the road.

➜ You are dead. Scrape yourself back together and get back to Chapter 2.

88.

You swing over to the drainpipe and manage to slowly slide your way down into the car park. It's only when you get to the bottom that you realise your mistake. The exit is heavily guarded, and cameras watch

86

87

88

every angle. Before you can climb back up, two policemen detain you and drag you back to the cells.

➔   You failed. The jury later find you guilty, and you are remanded in custody to await sentencing. Go back to Chapter 1.

89.

You run towards the ditch and jump down into the water. It stinks! Down here, in the stagnant, thigh-high water, it will be impossible for a dog to sniff you out. You push past dumped shopping trolleys and bike parts as the helicopter sweeps over you, but you're making slow progress. Up ahead you can see a large concrete pipe that must lead from a drain.

➔   If you decide to hide in the drain, go to 38.

➔   If you want to keep moving forward along the ditch, go to 5.

➔   If you want to climb out of the ditch on the other side and run towards the overpass, go to 43.

90.

You swerve across towards the open exit barrier, but just as you approach, the barrier arm swings down. It catches you across the chest, knocking you off the skateboard. The car behind you skids to a halt. There is nothing you can do as the suit seizes hold of you.

➜ You are never seen again. Get back to Chapter 5.

91.

The police officer lifts you to your feet as the rest of the tactical team move in. Mr Whiteman pushes through the crowd.

"Mr Whiteman! You got my message."

"Yes, yes. The police had the mall under surveillance and followed you here. Do you have the evidence?"

You kick the pager over to him and he bends down to pick it up.

"Keep it safe, Mr Whiteman. And whatever you do, don't press send."

CHAPTER SEVEN

The police take away the two suits, cuffing them and then loading them into waiting police vans.

In an interview room at the nearby police station, Mr Whiteman is alongside you as the detective runs through what happened.

"Your story checks out," he tells you. "You'll have to go through the proper channels, but you have no case to answer. The police force...owes you an apology."

"Mr Karin — the man who slipped you the gun and pager — was trying to kill the minister. But it seems he recognised one of the officers who were on guard duty, and he thought they would arrest him before he could set off the bomb."

"He aborted the assassination attempt, and gave the package with the gun to the first person he saw — you. What he intended to do was to use the pager to blow up the train as it came into the station. We've discovered explosives under the tracks at Central Station: a bomb big enough to destroy the whole station. Perhaps that's why Mr Karin wanted to get the pager back. Either he wanted to simply blow up the station, or maybe he just intended to destroy the evidence. No doubt that will come out under interrogation, er, I mean interview. You're free to go."

You look across at Mr Whiteman and smile.

CONGRATULATIONS YOU HAVE SURVIVED!

Have you tried **RÎVETS** short stories?

978 1 4451 1442 2 pb
978 1 4451 1443 9 eBook

You know when you do something that you instantly regret? That's how it starts for Greg. In the park, he sees it lying there: a black oblong of glass.

978 1 4451 1468 2 pb
978 1 4451 1471 2 eBook

Trev's sister is dead. Trev's mum is dead, and his dad.

The authorities think he did it. They won't believe him — that it was the house that took them.

978 1 4451 1467 5 pb
978 1 4451 1470 5 eBook

Miss Edwards had always smelled like a spring day — all honey and strawberries. Now she smells of rotten meat. Of terror. Of death. Josh's camping trip to a remote Welsh island has gone wrong. Horribly wrong...

978 1 4451 1466 8 pb
978 1 4451 1469 9 eBook

Tom Striker is a mudlark, earning a crust foraging on the banks of The Thames When Tom's friend Billy goes missing, and he saves a man claiming to be Old Father Thames, Tom is caught up in a battle between powerful spirits...

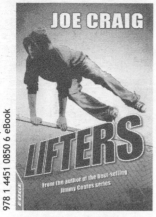

978 1 4451 0555 0 pb
978 1 4451 0850 6 eBook

Adaq and Maya steal on the streets to survive — a brother and sister team of "lifters". But when Adaq wants to quit his life of crime, Maya persuades him to do one last job. The only problem is, it might be the last thing Adaq ever does...

978 1 4451 0556 7 pb
978 1 4451 0849 0 eBook

Time is running out for the town of Fortunestone. It will take the strength of two boys to turn the tide, and a freak act of nature to bring them together...

978 1 4451 0557 4 pb
978 1 4451 1073 8 eBook

Mara's mother is missing, her little brother is sick, maybe dying, her father is grieving. It all seems hopeless — until Mara sets out on a life or death journey to bring her mother home...

978 1 4451 0707 3 pb
978 1 4451 1072 1 eBook

Carl is determined to become Warrior Number One in the online game "Warrior Warz". He must face the Dark Lord and his five-headed dragon.

978 1 4451 2345 5 pb
978 1 4451 2346 2 eBook

A dog. A helicopter. A soldier.
This book looks cool, eh?
War isn't cool, I've been there.
My name's Jamie, and inside I'll
tell you about two friends of
mine, Sam and Charlie, and how
they saved my life...

978 1 4451 2312 7 pb
978 1 4451 2315 8 eBook

Vulgar Pluck is in trouble.
He's tangled with the
wrong people and now he's
on the run. Vulgar needs to
get out of town — fast. But
first he's got one last job
to do. And he's got to do it
quick, before some really
dark magic is unleashed...

978 1 4451 2313 4 pb
978 1 4451 2316 5 eBook

Matt wakes up in a room
full of smoke. The smoke
is toxic. If he breathes it
in, he'll die. Matt is caught
up in a madman's plan
for revenge on his school.
But before Matt can save
his friends, he must save
himself...

978 1 4451 2311 0 pb
978 1 4451 12314 1 eBook

Imagine your very worst fear.
The kind of fear that visits
you in the middle of the night.
The kind of fear you keep
buried deep down. Tomasz
Kaczmarek knows all about that
kind of fear. And he's about to
find out what happens when
your worst fears come true...